KNOW ABOUT

Hi-Fi and Stereo

by Hans Fantel

EDITORS and ENGINEERS, LTD.

New Augusta, Indiana

FIRST EDITION

FIRST PRINTING — JUNE, 1965

KNOW ABOUT
HI-FI AND STEREO

Library of Congress Catalog Card Number: 65-21515

Fresh-frozen music? It seems like it! When this music is "thawed out" on an up-to-date high-fidelity music system, it loses none of its original flavor. Recorded and broadcast music can come vividly and freshly to life, retaining the full sense of reality.

When the same records are "warmed over" by ordinary radios and phonographs, they sound stale by comparison. Sure, the original tunes always remain recognizable. But this is also true of a tinkling music box. In a sense, ordinary radios and phonographs serve you only musical leftovers—what is left after the music gets hashed through inferior circuits. But there are more and more people who like to hear music that retains the zest of the original. These people realize that true tonal fidelity is not just for sophisticated tastes. They know that poor reproduction dulls the savor of the various instruments of voices, leaving the music flat and lifeless. It is for the ears of these more demanding listeners that high-fidelity sound reproduction was developed.

When high fidelity is spiced by the addition of stereo, musical realism goes a step farther. Not only is the sound truthfully transmitted, but the exact position of each player (or actor, or singer) can be sensed. So little is lost in reproduction that, with the best equipment now available, it is almost impossible to tell the difference between the original and what you hear in your living room.

You don't need a technical background to achieve top fidelity in your own home. It takes only a certain amount of general information. This book is written to give persons with no technical knowledge a basic acquaintance with audio and hi-fi equipment, to help them understand what they are buying, and how to plan their purchases sensibly. We hope that this book will help turn a musical famine into a musical feast.

At this point it only remains for me to add: Happy listening!

HANS FANTEL

CONTENTS

CHAPTER 1

CHAPTER 2

CHAPTER 3

CHAPTER 4

CHAPTER 5

CHAPTER 6

CHAPTER 7

WHAT IS HI-FI?

At first glance, music and science may seem poles apart, but today the bond between them has evolved into a fruitful working team. The average listener now reaps the benefit of this partnership by having at his fingertips more music than the richest man could command just a few decades ago. But to enjoy music in your home with the most satisfaction, it is helpful to have some knowledge of the equipment that produces the sound you hear.

First we must understand the sound of music itself. This is the raw material as well as the end product of high fidelity. Music is the stuff that goes into the microphone and ultimately pours from the speaker.

The sound of music consists of vibrations in the air. When Heifetz plays his violin or Al Hirt toots his horn, they impart vibrations to the air around their instruments. These pulses spread in the air like the ring of waves you create when you throw a pebble into a pond. Even your voice is an instrument for setting up these waves—strictly speaking, pressure pulses—in the air. When these pulses reach the ear, the brain interprets these signals as sound. The personal experience of sound takes place only within your head. The special quirks of human response are one of the important factors in sound engineering.

The most astonishing thing about sound is its limitless variety. It is a long way from the lowest note of the organ to the highest note of the piccolo, but a good sound system must reproduce all the sounds in between, plus their overtones, in order to create that feeling of naturalness that spells high fidelity.

PITCH

When you listen to a melody, you notice that some notes are higher and others are lower. We call this difference *pitch*. What we perceive as pitch is determined by the rapidity with which the sound pulses vibrate in the air. If the vibrations are very quick, we hear a high note; if they are slow, we hear a low note. This rate of vibration is called *frequency,* and one complete vibration is called a *cycle*.

Are we suddenly getting technical? Not at all. The term cycle has exactly the same meaning here as in such familiar expressions as "weather cycle" or the "cycles" of the stock market. It simply means that the process repeats itself—that the vibrations follow each other at regular intervals and thereby create the pitch.

All this can be summed up in what we may call the first principle of sound: Each musical note has a certain *pitch* determined by its *frequency,* that is, the number of vibrations (or cycles) in a given time.

Frequency is usually stated in the number of *cycles per second* (abbreviated as *cps*)—a basic term in the specifications of sound equipment. The lowest note the average human ear can hear is about 20 cps; the roll of distant thunder might be heard as low as 16 cps.

The high limit of hearing varies from person to person. As a rule, only children and adolescents can hear extremely high frequencies around 20,000 cps. The upper limit of adult hearing generally lies around 16,000 cps, and declines with age to about 10,000 cps or less.

We cannot assign a definite pitch to all sounds—for example, the sound of water rushing full force into a bathtub, or a burst of applause. These are noises, sounds made up of a random mixture of unrelated frequencies. Since these vibrations have no regular rate of recurrence, we cannot speak of them as having any pitch.

TONE COLOR

Tone color, or timbre as it is sometimes called, is yet another vital element of sound. It is especially important in the case of music. A cello and a trombone may be playing the same note, but you can easily tell them apart. Each has a characteristic tone color. What accounts for this?

When scientists began to analyze sounds about a hundred years ago, they discovered that what we hear as a single musical note actually consists of many tones. The pitch that our ear identifies as the basic note is called the *fundamental*. But the fundamental frequency carries with it a whole series of additional frequencies called *overtones,* or *harmonics.* These are simple multiples of the fundamental frequency (that is, the basic pitch frequency $\times 2$, $\times 3$, $\times 4$, etc.). Not all of these overtones are equally strong. Each instrument has its own pattern of strength and weakness among its overtones. This individual overtone pattern gives each instrument its distinctive tone color, or timbre.

From this it becomes apparent why a broad and uniform range of frequency response is essential in a good sound system. Suppose an oboe is playing a 1500 cps note; its overtones will be:

$$
\begin{array}{rll}
3000 & \text{cps} & (= 1500 \text{ cps} \times 2) \\
4500 & \text{cps} & (= 1500 \text{ cps} \times 3) \\
6000 & \text{cps} & (= 1500 \text{ cps} \times 4) \\
7500 & \text{cps} & (= 1500 \text{ cps} \times 5) \\
9000 & \text{cps} & (= 1500 \text{ cps} \times 6) \\
10{,}500 & \text{cps} & (= 1500 \text{ cps} \times 7) \\
12{,}000 & \text{cps} & (= 1500 \text{ cps} \times 8)
\end{array}
$$

and so on to the upper limit of hearing. To do justice to

the sound of the oboe, the system must reproduce all these overtones in the exact proportion in which they naturally occur. It must neither emphasize nor suppress any of these frequencies. The same applies to all the other instruments.

Even low-pitched instruments like the bass fiddle, the tuba, and the kettledrum send out high-frequency overtones that give them their particular tonal flavor.

Chart 1-1. Approximate Frequency Range of Various Musical Instruments and Familiar Sounds.

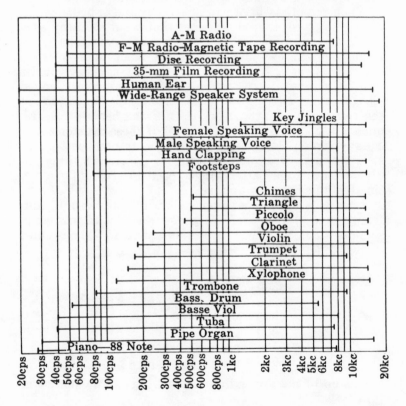

From this it is easy to see that high fidelity depends on the true reproduction of these overtones.

So put down another basic principle: *Tone color is produced by overtone patterns.* To give you the true character of music, a high-fidelity system must have therefore a wide frequency range (at least to 15,000 cps) in order to reproduce these overtones. The frequency ranges of various instruments are shown in Chart 1-1. In this chart, the fundamentals of the musical tones go up to about 5000 cps. Everything above that is an overtone of the pitches of those instruments. When we speak in thousands of cycles it is customary to use the term *kilocycles* (kilo = 1000) ; thus, in the table, 5000 cycles is listed as 5 kilocycles per second (abbreviated as 5 kc).

LOUDNESS

Every sound also has a certain loudness, or volume as it is loosely called. Differences in loudness are caused by differences in the energy of the sound. Suppose you knock at a door. If nobody answers, you bang louder the second time. By this commonplace action you have demonstrated the physical difference between soft and loud sounds. In order to produce the louder knock you had to put more energy into it. Or, to put it the other way around, louder sounds have a greater energy content.

Since sound is motion of the air, we must try to visualize both pitch and loudness in terms of motion. Let us return to the idea of sound waves resembling the ripples on the surface of a pond. Those rings of ripples which were spaced close together would be the equivalent of high notes because a great many ripples would reach the edge of the pond in a short space of time (high frequency). Broader ripples spaced farther apart would be the equivalent of low notes because they would strike the edge of the pond (be received) at longer intervals of time (low frequency).

Now suppose we dropped a bigger and heavier rock into the pool instead of a little pebble. The heavier rock would take more energy to throw it into the middle of the pool, and when it hit the water it would make bigger ripples. These bigger ripples would be the equivalent of louder sounds, and would, of course, strike the edge of the pool with more force (greater energy). The height of these waves is a measure of their energy content. In the language of physical measurement, the height of these waves is called their *amplitude*. As our third basic principle, therefore, we can say that the *amplitude* of a sound wave determines whether it is loud or soft. Pitch, loudness, and color are shown graphically in Fig. 1-1.

SOUND AND ELECTRICITY

Many people are puzzled by the mysterious notion of music running through a wire. The change of sound into electricity and back again always seems something of a miracle. True, it is a commonplace miracle, but it may strike you as somewhat marvelous every time you pick up the telephone and hear a voice talking.

What is involved here is the transformation of sound energy into some kind of electrical equivalent that retains the characteristics of the original sound. What characteristics? Those we have just explained—the fundamental and overtone frequencies, and the amplitude.

You may find it helpful to think of an electric current as a plastic conveyor belt moving at high speed. If we make this flexible belt undulate exactly like the sound waves we want to hear, then it becomes a carrier of sound. In effect, sound (or rather, the waveform of sound) rides piggyback on the electric current.

The process of putting sound patterns into an electric current is called *modulation*. We say that an electric current has been modulated when it assumes the patterns of the music or speech that we want to reproduce. Thus transformed into an electric *signal,* music and speech can be amplified, recorded, or sent out via radio. It is in this electric guise that music makes its journey through time and space into your living room.

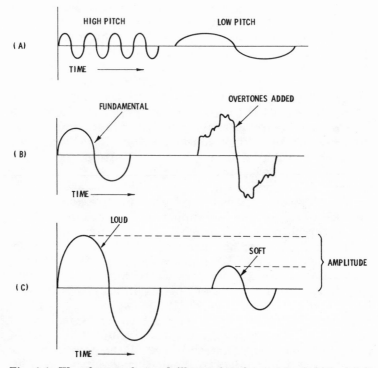

Fig. 1-1. Waveforms of sound illustrating frequency (which determines pitch), amplitude (which determines loudness), and the effect of overtones (which determines tone color).

YOU ARE STEREO

Stereo was "invented" millions of years ago when two-eyed, two-eared creatures first appeared on the earth. You perceive the world from two points of view with your eyes and two ears. That is what gives you your sense of depth, and makes your senses of sight and sound three-dimensional. Your stereophonic ears give a sense of the direction to the sounds you hear.

Well, you might say, if stereo is millions of years old, what's all the shouting about. Granted, stereo inside your head is nothing new, but stereo in music-reproducing systems is a major technical breakthrough. It enables us to hear records and radio broadcasts with the natural stereo dimension we were born with.

THE STEREO EFFECT

The reason why we have pairs of ears (and eyes) is not just to have a spare in case one gives out. No, it is to help us live more effectively in the three-dimensional space we inhabit. When you look at an object with your two eyes, you get an idea of its position in space with a precision that is lacking when you look at it with just one eye. When you look through a stereoscopic viewer with one eye only, everything in the picture goes flat. If you still don't believe how important stereoscopic vision is, try threading a needle with one of your eyes closed.

Something similar holds true for stereophonic hearing. It gives an idea about the space in which the sound is made—an impression not possible with one-eared listening. Since each of your ears points in a different direction, they never hear exactly the same sounds. Suppose a car honks its horn at you as you cross the street. Your head jerks instantly toward the sound. How did you know which way to look? The ear aimed at the car heard the sound more loudly than the one turned away from it. Also, the ear nearer the car heard the sound sooner, for sound takes time to travel around your head to reach the other ear. From these tiny differences in loudness and time of arrival, your brain computes the approximate direction and distance of the sound source; that is stereo hearing. Blindfolded you can tell the approximate size of the room you are in by the way sound is reflected from the walls. Your own voice sounds different to you in the narrow confines of a telephone booth, or in the wide spaces of a big church. You have, in short, a sense of *acoustic* space.

This sense of acoustic space is musically important, too. If you were blindfolded at a concert, you could still spot the positions of the different players. Even with your eyes closed, you could follow what was going on with the fiddles on the left, the winds in the middle, and the cellos at the right. You would even be able to tell that the sound of the percussion was coming from behind the rest of the orchestra.

This kind of stereo hearing contributes to your understanding of the music. When many instruments are playing different things at the same time, this kind of separation makes it easier to hear each strand of melody standing out clearly against its background.

STEREO REPRODUCTION

Well, you say, "I always listen to records with both ears, so what's the point?" The point is that listening to *monophonic* (nonstereo) radios or phonographs is no better than listening with one ear because in mono you are listening to a sound that was "heard" by the recording equipment through only one ear; played back to you through mono playback systems you can't get more than a "one-ear's view" of the original sound.

The purpose of stereo sound equipment is to retain the space factors of music. Stereo recordings and broadcasts are now made with "two ears," that is, with two sets of microphones instead of one, both recording into separate channels (Figs. 1-2 and 1-3). Between them they preserve those small but vital differences between what your left and right ears hear at an actual performance. With stereo sound equipment you can now have the same experience at home.

Stereo captures the whole shape and feel of the original performance and transplants it into your living room. It does even better than that: It frees you from your living room. You get the astonishing feeling that the walls are being pushed back and that you really are in the cabaret, the concert hall, the cathedral, the opera house, or wherever the recording was made. No longer does the sound seem to squirt out at you from the speakers. Instead, it seems to flow broadly from the entire area between *and beyond* the speakers. In other words, stereo delivers the music to you in its natural acoustical setting.

Fig. 1-2. A recording session at Columbia Records Studio, seen from above, shows the physical layout of the various instruments in the orchestra The stereo effect pinpoints the position of the players in playback.

By contrast, a single channel "mono" radio or record player can render music only as a one-eared person hears it. The element of acoustic space is missing.

Granted, stereo sound is not a simple concept. It's easy enough to distinguish a three dimensional object such as a bottle from a two dimensional picture of the bottle. But to form an idea of something intangible, such as sound, in three dimensions is not easy. It is not surprising that a great deal of confusion and downright misinformation persist about stereo.

Some beginners believe that you can get stereo results simply by hooking up an extra speaker to a monophonic phonograph. Nothing could be farther from the truth,

Courtesy Columbia Records, Inc.

Fig. 1-3. Capturing musical realism as heard in the studio—that is the job of stereo high fidelity.

because the two speakers would receive identical signals from the one channel in the system. That vital difference between the two ears would be missing.

Confusion is often expressed by questions like, "Is stereo better than hi-fi?" This reflects the notion that stereo is something to replace high fidelity. The question is meaningless, for stereo has nothing to do with the basic quality of the sound you hear. Stereo simply means two-channel sound, and this may be anywhere from amazingly lifelike down to incredibly bad.

You can easily get stereo without high fidelity—any cheap table-model stereo phonograph can give you that. The sound may be distorted, lacking a full round bass, choked of its brilliant luster—but it will be stereo. The answer to the question "Is stereo better than hi-fi?" is that stereo has simply got to be hi-fi if it is going to be any good!

Stereo in itself cannot make up for the shortcomings of sound equipment. Stereo or not, fidelity remains the first requirement of good sound.

It is important to remember these three basic facts about stereo and hi-fi:

1. Stereo is no substitute for sound quality.
2. To be musically satisfying, stereo must meet high-fidelity standards.
3. Stereo is a "plus" factor (something added to high fidelity) but fidelity remains first and foremost in importance.

To sum up, stereo can do more than hi-fi, but it cannot do it without high fidelity.

THE PARTS OF A HI-FI SYSTEM

In order to reproduce music in your own home you need a number of parts called *components* (Fig. 1-4). Whether your taste runs to an integrated console or separate components, the elements are the same. The following chapters deal with the "hardware" of high fidelity, and will help you to know more about the components you buy and use.

First, let us list the components that make up a sound system and describe their functions.

The TURNTABLE is the rotating platter that spins the record.

The TONE ARM carries the phono cartridge across the record.

Fig. 1-4. An attractive home installation combines built-in components with the open-shelf approach. At the extreme right are a Harman-Kardon *Citation* stereo amplifier, preamplifier, and tuner. The bottom cabinet houses tape recorder and speakers. A Weathers manual record player and a Miracord automatic changer are placed open on the shelves.

The CARTRIDGE is the little unit containing a stylus (sometimes called "needle") which traces the grooves of your record. The cartridge turns the vibrations of the stylus into variations in an electric current.

The AMPLIFIER has two sections: The PREAMPLIFIER, and the POWER AMPLIFIER. The preamplifier contains the various controls needed to operate the system. The power amplifier makes the signal strong enough to drive the speakers.

The SPEAKER is the voice of your sound system, turning the amplifier electric currents into sounds.

The TUNER picks up radio signals (am, fm, or fm-stereo) from the air and feeds them into your system so that they can be reproduced through the amplifiers and speakers.

The TAPE RECORDER (Fig. 1-4) is an optional unit that can be made to function as a part of the total sound system.

These are the basic components of a system. The following chapters will discuss them in detail.

CHAPTER 2

THE RECORD PLAYER

High-fidelity stereo records make the world's great musicians your permanent house guests. They are always ready for a command performance. You select the program, you choose the hour. And you don't even have to dress for the occasion. Perhaps you'll be the only listener—relaxed, absorbed, and carried beyond your everyday problems. Or maybe you prefer to invite friends to join you at a lifelike re-creation of the latest from Broadway—complete with the original cast and a casual snack at intermission. Events from the world's greatest concert halls or the hottest jazz joints—all these come alive through reliable components.

CHANGERS, TURNTABLES, OR AUTOMATIC TURNTABLES?

For playing records on a component music system you need either a record changer or a turntable fitted with a tone arm. Record changers are, in effect, combinations of tone arms and turntables with built-in automation. They will provide hours of uninterrupted music without your touching them, and then turn themselves off when they have run through their stack of discs. Many ordinary changers are not manufactured to high-fidelity standards and will fail to liberate all of the sound in the record grooves. Often they will wear out the records much faster than true high-fidelity equipment.

Fig. 2-1. Recent example of a top-quality record changer is the Garrard *Lab-80* automatic turntable. Its wooden tone arm is non-resonant, precision-balanced in low-friction bearings. It can be remotely controlled through cueing levers to prevent possible stylus damage due to awkward handling.

For high quality performance, the same standards apply to changers as to component turntables and tone arms. To separate high-fidelity record changers from the ordinary variety, the term "automatic turntable" (Fig. 2-1) has been coined to mark those units which meet the higher standards. Their hallmark is careful workmanship and adaptability. However, many listeners prefer to buy a manually operated turntable and tone arm (Fig. 2-2).

TURNTABLE TIPS

While all other components of a stereo system are involved with the actual sounds passing through the system,

Fig. 2-2. Three popular high-quality turntables with pre-mounted tone arms provide top-grade sound at moderate prices and eliminate the need for installing the tone arm. They are the Acoustic Research AR-turntable, the Bogen Model B-62, and the Rek-O-Kut. The Bogen offers four-speed operation with variable speed control and tone-arm control by means of a lever to prevent accidental dropping of arm. The AR model has a viscous-damped arm that floats down harmlessly to the record surface if dropped.

the turntable and the tone arm remain mute. They are the silent partners of the business. However, like most silent partners, they have a lot to say about how the business is run.

Rumble

Staying silent is by no means easy for a turntable. Like any other rotating device, it is prone to vibration. This vibration is picked up by the phono cartridge along with music. This is the notorious *turntable rumble*—a sound like softly rolling thunder, and an unwelcome accompaniment to your music. If you have speakers with good bass response, they will pass the rumble right along with the music.

The only way to eliminate rumble is by means of a smooth-running turntable motor and precision-machined and carefully fitted bearings and parts. The rotating parts must be balanced and finished to fine tolerances. Such manufacturing techniques don't come cheap, which explains why a quality turntable (Fig. 2-3) is really worth its price.

Besides keeping all tolerances close, vibration is reduced by suspending the drive motor in elastic shock

Fig. 2-3. Bottom view of the Thorens TD-124 turntable reveals the precision aluminum casting, carefully shielded motor, and other construction details revealing the quality of this Swiss-made four-speed turntable with variable speed control.

mounts. These absorb a significant part of the motor's noise. Moreover, motor vibration is isolated from the turntable by an elastic transmission—usually in the form of a plastic belt that filters out most of the remaining rumble.

Rumble can never be completely eliminated. Most responsible manufacturers will state exactly how much rumble their machines have. Their specifications will usually read something like: "Rumble = −35 db." This means that the rumble is 35 units of "loudness" *less* than a standard test tone. That figure of 35 db, by the way, is the minimum requirement of the National Association of Broadcasters (NAB). On a speaker system with good bass response, this sound would still be slightly audible. A turntable with −45 db rumble would seem almost silent.

Most test records have a band of silent grooves. If you play them, you should not be able to hear any rumble at all. Be sure that your tone controls are in the "flat" position, that is, without the bass turned up beyond the *normal* point. If you play a test record with the bass boosted, no turntable could pass the test.

Wow and Flutter

The turntable motor must spin the platter at a rock-steady rate. If the motor won't pull evenly the chugging causes a wavering of the pitch called *flutter*. Flutter is a kind of tonal shiver, a quivering quality of the sound that shows up especially badly on long-held notes. Uneven motor speed may also show up in the form of *wow*. This is a slow up and down waver like that of a police siren. Wow and flutter can make the best recorded performances unbearable.

Quality turntables avoid wow and flutter by using motors with a highly uniform pull (or *torque* if you prefer the technical term for rotary force). They attain this by using precision motors with four or more poles. The greater the number of poles used in the design of the motor, the smoother its motion will become. Some of the best turntables use what are called *hysteresis-synchronous* motors, whose pull remains constant throughout each turn. The speed of these motors is largely unaffected by line-voltage changes—a point to consider if you live out in the country where voltage is likely to vary.

The flywheel effect of the turntable platter itself helps to smooth out the rotation. For this reason, a fine turntable must be carefully machined, well balanced, and smoothly set in its bearings.

To keep wow and flutter within acceptable limits, the turntable motion should be constant within 1 percent. On very good turntables, wow and flutter may be as low as 0.1 percent. A good informal test for wow and flutter is to play a record with long-sustained piano chords. Observe if the tone remains steady. Such sustained piano music shows up pitch variations very clearly. However, be sure that the waver, if there is any, is not on the record itself. Try different records. Most test records have special sections to test for wow and flutter. These are long steady tones which quickly reveal any variations of turntable speed.

Speed Accuracy

If your turntable spins at a rock-steady rate, this is fine, but it is not enough. It must also turn at exactly the proper rate. If it turns too fast, the music will sound too high. Voices will sound very shrill. If the turntable is too slow, the music will sound lower, more dull and soggy. Turntable speed should be accurate within 1 percent, or better. A *stroboscopic disc* provides a simple way of checking speed accuracy. Many machines have such a disc built in. If not, you can buy a stroboscopic disc to be placed on your turntable for just a few cents at your high-fidelity store.

If you like to play a musical instrument along with the recorded music, you may require a turntable with variable speed adjustment. This permits you to tune the turntable's speed until the pitch of the music matches the pitch of your instrument. This control may also help to make up for speed changes due to changes in your supply of electricity.

At present there are two trends in turntable design. One might be called the battleship approach (Figs. 2-4 and 2-5). It relies on heavy, massive construction to increase the flywheel effect of the platter in smoothing out the rotation. The other approach might be called the bantam approach. It is exactly the opposite in method. It stresses lightness as a way of keeping vibration low enough to be effectively controlled. Both methods lead

Fig. 2-4. The heavy "battleship" school of turntable design is exemplified by the Empire *Troubador*, which features a carefully machined and precision balanced 6-lb belt-driven platter and a dynamically balanced tone arm.

to excellent results in the right hands. Do not judge a turntable by weight alone. Some extremely light bantam designs may outperform some of the costly battleships.

You will also have to decide whether to get a single-speed or a multispeed turntable. If you have a collection

Fig. 2-5. The Dual 1009 automatic changer with its heavy platter and dynamically balanced tone arm offers performance on par with professional-type manually operated turntables and tone arms.

of old 78-rpm discs, you will need a machine capable of playing them. If not, this feature would be a waste of money. You will hardly find any use for speeds other than the standard 33⅓ rpm at which almost all LP's (both mono and stereo) are recorded. With the exception of a few very special discs designed for the connoisseur, almost everything worthwhile that has been recorded at 45 rpm is also available on 33⅓-rpm records. People with many old 78's, which aren't hi-fi anyway, sometimes get a changer for them, and play their LP's on a single-speed turntable.

Fig. 2-6. The Thorens TD-121 turntable represents the ancient tradition of Swiss craftsmanship applied to the new science of high-fidelity stereo.

TONE ARMS—THE LIGHT TOUCH

On casual acquaintance, a tone arm is just a sort of stick on a swivel. All it has to do is hold the cartridge in place—or so it seems to the beginner.

Actually, a good tone arm has to meet some pretty stringent requirements. Its job is to carry the cartridge across the disc. If the cartridge doesn't get a good, smooth ride all the way, it will complain. You will hear these complaints in the form of distortion.

Almost any phono cartridge will sound better if you give it a chance in a good tone arm. Moreover, a good arm can save a lot of wear on your records and stylus. Badly designed and cheaply made tone arms are the only kind you ever see on the common low-fi phonographs. They have many shortcomings: They jump grooves. They garble the sound. They hasten the wear of both your discs and stylus with their excessive weight and stiffness.

A good, component type of tone arm is a matter of pure economy. It pays for itself in what it saves in record wear alone. But besides saving your discs, it pays real dividends in tone quality. This will probably surprise a lot of hi-fiers who think that the tone arm makes no difference in the sound. An arm generates no signal, nor does it amplify, or reproduce, a signal. "So," they ask, "how can it have anything to do with the music?"

Quite a lot! It makes no sense to have a high-quality sound system if your arm is going to spoil everything from the start. The tone arm must guide the cartridge over an intricately calculated path. It must keep all friction down to the minimum. It must apply a constant and correct downward pressure. It must not be disturbed by warped records or by floor vibration. It must ride lightly enough to protect your records. Only a capable tone arm can help your cartridge to "read" all the delicate details of the sound recorded into the wiggling grooves (Fig. 2-7).

Fig. 2-7. The music starts here. This enlarged view shows a diamond stylus tracing the musical waveforms in the groove of a stereo record. Extreme tracing accuracy—a condition for true fidelity—is attained by high-quality cartridges and tone arms.

This goes double for stereo. Here the stylus must trace a vertical pattern as well as a sideways one. Consequently, stereo demands much finer qualities in a tone arm than mono.

There are four basic requirements that all tone arms must meet if they are to do their job properly.

Accurate Tracking

The arm must keep the cartridge lined up so that it travels across the record in a straight line—or as nearly straight as possible. We would like the cartridge to lie along a line tangent to the record grooves. But this is impossible for all of the grooves on the record because the diameter gets smaller as the stylus moves in toward the center. The difference between the ideal position and the true position of the cartridge at various points on the record is called the *tracking error*. The maximum tracking error should not exceed two degrees in a good tone arm.

The funny curves and angles you see on many arms are the result of some fancy figuring with the hard facts of geometry. Audio designers have produced some ingenious twists in their efforts to keep tracking error within bounds. They have learned how to make the tracking error of a fine tone arm quite harmless to the sound. Of course, the arm must be mounted with great care at exactly the right distance from the center of the turntable if you want to get optimum results (Fig. 2-8).

Accurate tracking is even more important in stereo. If the tone arm makes the stylus lean more heavily against one side of the record groove than the other, the stereo channels won't balance properly and the sound becomes distorted.

Constant Stylus Force

The phono cartridge should ride the record grooves at a certain downward pressure. This is called the *stylus force*. Every high-quality tone arm has a device that will allow you to adjust the stylus force to the specifications for the particular cartridge you are using.

There are several ways of allowing for this adjustment. Cheap low-fi phonographs simply use an upward spring pressure to lighten the arm. This is the least dependable method because it makes the arm rather jumpy. Floor vibrations caused by heavy footsteps or passing traffic tend to make the spring-balanced arms skip grooves.

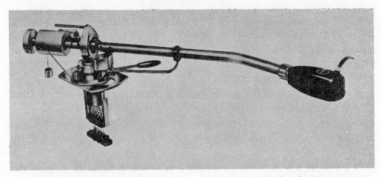

Fig. 2-8. The Shure-SME arm, produced in England, features an elaborate gimbal suspension with precision bearings, designed to minimize friction in both lateral and vertical movement. A lever control gently places the arm on the desired spot on the record. Precise positioning-control adjustments for the pivot point minimize tracking error.

Many hi-fi arms use a light *downward* spring pressure counterbalanced by an adjustable sliding weight. This type of system is known as "dynamic balance" (Fig. 2-9). It needs readjustment from time to time to compensate for possible weakening of the spring. But "dynamic balance" provides particularly accurate tracking of both sides of the groove even if the turntable tilts.

Another system employed in the better arms relies on static balance (Fig. 2-10). It uses no springs—just a sliding counterweight to regulate the stylus pressure. This system has the virtue of simplicity. Once set, no adjustment is ever needed. However, it must be mounted

Fig. 2-9. Dynamically balanced arms track records, even when the turntable is tilted, as demonstrated by this exhibition display of an Empire turntable and arm.

on an absolutely level surface where it will not be in danger of sudden shocks or vibration from the floor.

Nonresonance

As your record spins, the stylus shivers its way around the grooves. If the arm also vibrates, the stylus cannot trace the groove accurately. It needs a steady hold at one end. A tone arm that vibrates along with the frantic dance of the stylus is said to be *resonating* to the stylus movement. This makes hash of the recorded sound.

A good tone arm must resist the temptation to join the rhythm of the stylus. In other words, it must be non-

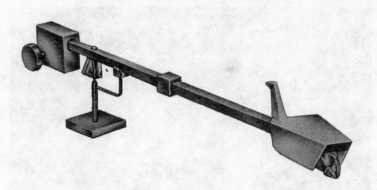

Fig. 2-10. Stanton's *Unipoise* arm achieves low friction by being pivoted on a single point. It is statically balanced by an adjustable counterweight.

resonant. The best designs attempt to avoid resonance by using tubular members, special nonresonating materials (Fig. 2-11), and other devices aimed at keeping the arm's own resonance below the audible range.

Fig. 2-11. Grado tone arm is made of fine gunstock walnut, a material inherently free of resonance. Note various adjustments for precision setting of dynamic balance.

Low Friction

Friction is a drag—literally! Any friction in the pivot of the tone arm will cause it to resist the motion of the cartridge across the disc. This makes the stylus press harder against the outer wall of the groove than against the inner wall; the result is distortion. In stereo, it will also destroy the balance between the channels—two headaches for the price of one!

Some arms minimize friction by using ball bearings at their pivots. Some arms rest on a single needle point to allow free motion. Knife-edge pivots (like those used in chemical balances) are employed in other designs.

Because good cartridges are extremely sensitive to rough handling, some tone arms have some sort of safety device to prevent damage to the cartridge. Some have viscous-damping fluid in their bearings which lets the arm float gently down toward the record if it is accidentally dropped. Others have automatic positioning devices which allow the arm to be lowered gently onto the disc by a lever control. This protects both record and cartridge.

Installing a tone arm is a tricky business. Unless you are an experienced hand with a drill, you would do well to leave this job to your dealer. However, some excellent record-playing equipment comes with the tone arm mounted on the turntable base. This eliminates a tricky mounting chore, and ensures a good match between the characteristics of the arm and turntable.

PHONO CARTRIDGES

When you hear a smooth, high trumpet note from your speakers, it may be a pleasure for you, but it's no fun for your stylus. Your cartridge (Fig. 2-12) has to make an agonizing journey of hairpin turns to give you that note (as many as 18,000 turns each second). In stereo the stylus (Fig. 2-13) gets an added thrill: it flies up and down in addition to swinging from side to side. Yet,

Fig. 2-12. Despite its smallness, the stereo cartridge is one of the most important parts of the entire system. Its quality largely determines whether the sound you hear is true to the original. The model shown here is a Stanton *Fluxvalve 500AT* with frequency response from 20 to 20,000 cps and 35-db channel separation.

in spite of this terrific beating to the stylus, the groove tracing must remain painstakingly true to the musical waveform.

There is a marked difference in the tonal quality of different cartridge designs. Some have a warm, rounded sound that seems to emphasize the blending of instruments. Others have a sharp, crisp sound that seems to pick out the individual instruments rather than the over-all blend. The choice between these types is a matter of taste.

There are two basic types of cartridge: ceramic and magnetic. As a rule, ceramic cartriges are the less expensive type. However, most ceramics do not match the performance of magnetic cartridges. For this reason, most high-fidelity installations employ magnetic cartridges. All modern stereo cartridges are quite delicate and are easily damaged by rough handling. Treat your cartridge with care and it will treat your ears and your records just as considerately.

The cartridge is the first vital link in your sound system. As the starting point of the signal in your system, it largely determines the quality of the sound you hear. So don't underestimate the importance of your cartridge just because it is the smallest and least conspicuous of all components. The performance of a cartridge is determined by several design factors which we shall briefly discuss.

High Compliance

A high-compliance cartridge is one whose stylus requires very little force to make it follow the wiggles in

Fig. 2-13. Shure's V-15 Stereo Dynatic cartridge with its elliptically shaped stylus is a deluxe model. It is capable of tracking records at less than one gram pressure when mounted in a good tone arm.

the record groove. The specifications for compliance may look forbidding, but they are really quite easy to interpret. For instance, in a statement like:

$$\text{compliance} = 12 \times 10^{-6} \text{ cm/dyne}$$

you just watch the number before the multiplication sign. If it is 10 or higher, you have nothing to worry about. And you can forget about the rest of that complex expression. A figure of 10 or better means that the stylus follows the zigzags of the groove quite easily. Besides, it causes very little record wear, and the diamond tip of the stylus will last longer. For a compliance greater than 10 you'd better have a really good tone arm. Only a fine arm is capable of carrying such a cartridge lightly enough. Incidentally, for best stereo performance, the compliance should be the same measured vertically as it is horizontally.

Small Dynamic Mass

This simply means that the moving parts of the cartridge should weigh as little as possible. The lighter they are, the easier the cartridge can maneuver its twisting road along the record groove. First-rate cartridges have a dynamic mass of 3 mg (= 3 milligrams) or less. A milligram is a very small weight, less than 0.000035 ounce. Some cartridges have a dynamic mass as small as that, or even smaller.

Low Tracking Force

The effective weight of the stylus in the groove is called the *tracking force* (or *stylus pressure*). Some high-compliance cartridges track at weights of one or two grams, because they require very little force to move the stylus. When the tone arm has been balanced to carry the cartridge at such low tracking forces, the wear on your records is negligible. However, only a first-class arm is able to track a cartridge at such featherweight pressures; so, we're back to that again.

Uniform Frequency Response

A good cartridge must cover the entire range of audible frequencies (that is from about 30 cps up to 18,000 cps). Some of the best cartridges reach beyond 20,000 cps. Frequency response should not only be wide, it should also be *flat* (uniform) throughout its range. The manufacturer's specifications are generally represented by symbols like ±2 db. This means that throughout the cartridge's given range of frequencies, no frequency will vary more than two loudness units (db) from the proper value. If this deviation does not exceed ± 3 db for the entire range of the cartridge, the sound of your music will be very smooth indeed.

Clean Stereo Separation

A stereo cartridge must be able to track a stereo groove in such a way that the two channels stay separated. If the signal from one channel leaks into the other, this "crosstalk" will cancel the stereo effect. Actually there is always a small amount of such leakage. The practical problem is to keep this leakage at a minimum. The specifications of a good cartridge express its ability to separate the two channels as to the difference in loudness between the signal and the leak. It will usually be stated in terms like:

crosstalk at 1000 cps: −20 db

This means that the cartridge will keep the "leak" of a 1000-cycle tone 20 loudness units lower than the proper signal of that channel. Such a slight amount of "crosstalk" is almost inaudible. At higher frequencies, say 10,000 cps, separation may get as low as −15 db and still be quite good.

Stylus Style

Some of the most recent developments in cartridge design concern just the stylus tip. In the newest cartridges, the stylus is set at a 15-degree angle to the record surface.

This new positioning allows a cleaner sound to come through your cartridge than was possible before. Look for this detail (the 15-degree angle) in the specifications of any cartridge you buy. It's one way to tell an old model from a new one. Another stylus development is its shape. Some tips are now formed as cones with an elliptical (that is, oval) cross section. This new shape allows the stylus to follow the tiny turns in the groove with greater accuracy. Of course, it is not easy to shape a diamond to this unusual form; therefore an elliptical stylus costs more than a round one. The resultant improvement in sound is small and is often noticeable only toward the center of the disc (nearer the label) where the musical waveforms in the grooves are more crowded. For many customers it may be debatable whether this small improvement is worth the increase in the price of the cartridge.

We have been talking about styli under the assumption that you will buy one with a diamond tip. A diamond is more expensive, of course, but it pays for itself in two ways: first, it lasts at least 10 times longer than a sapphire and therefore saves in replacement costs; second because it keeps its shape longer, it won't wear out your records until about 3000 or 4000 hours of playing. As they say in the ads, "a diamond is forever"—almost.

CHAPTER 3

THE AMPLIFIER

The amplifier is the nerve center of your music system. It receives the tiny electrical impulses from your phono cartridge, radio tuner, or tape recorder, and amplifies (enlarges) them until they become strong enough to drive the speakers. It also accommodates an input selector for switching among tape, tuner, or record player; and the controls for adjusting volume, treble, bass, stereo balance, and other operating factors.

The part which contains the controls is called the *preamplifier* (Fig. 3-1). The part which sends power to the speakers is the *power amplifier* (Fig. 3-2). Most modern amplifiers are integrated; that is, they contain a preamp and a power amplifier (Fig. 3-3) combined into a single component. Only where very high output power is required are preamplifier and power amplifier designed as separate units.

THE TRANSISTOR REVOLUTION

The new words are "solid state." Nearly all the new components designed today are solid state—that is, with transistors instead of tubes. Not too long ago, transistors (Fig. 3-4) were often temperamental. But today, under the impetus of space science and with refinement of automated manufacturing techniques, transistors are thoroughly reliable workhorses. A whole new concept of electronic design has arisen. The transistor, formerly good enough only for pocket portables, is now a member in good standing on the high-fidelity team. Whole generations of tube designs have been scrapped and replaced with the transistor concept.

What accounts for this upheaval? Compared with tubes, the transistor has many advantages. Transistors are much

Fig. 3-1. Dynaco's PAS-3 stereo preamplifier is one of the most popular top-quality kits. This control unit can be combined with any of Dynaco's power amplifier kits.

sturdier than tubes; they can stand accidental knocks that would finish most tubes. Unlike tubes, transistors can stand continued vibration without producing erratic noises—as the engineers say, they are nonmicrophonic. They draw less power, and they don't get as hot as tubes. It takes less time for a transistor to warm up. Transistors do not change their performance values with age, and theoretically, at least, they never wear out.

Transistors have one other advantage which makes them especially suited for high fidelity; they are inherently humfree. What does this mean to the listener? Perhaps the most underrated pleasure of high fidelity is

Fig. 3-2. The McIntosh 275, a real powerhouse of an amplifier, represents the super-deluxe approach to stereo. It pumps out 75 watts per channel with minimum distortion—enough to fill a mansion with life-size sound. At these high power levels, separate preamplifiers and power amplifiers are employed.

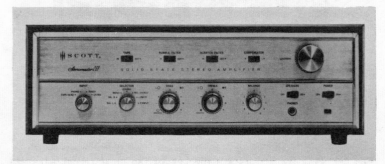

Fig. 3-3. Scott's latest amplifier is an all-transistor design delivering 40 watts per channel with many up-to-date circuit refinements and elaborate control facilities.

the satisfaction of hearing your music reproduced against a quiet background. Whenever ordinary radio phonographs are turned on, the first thing we hear is the hum and buzz of the current. Most of us take this almost for granted as a background to recorded music. Transistors are so much quieter than tubes that the music seems to emerge against a background of sheer silence.

Audio fans have coined the term "transistor sound" to describe the extraordinary qualities that the solid state revolution has brought to hi-fi. Transistor sound is characterized by clear definition of individual instruments

Courtesy Hughes Aircraft Co.

Fig. 3-4. Tiny transistors are the key to the most recent advances in high-fidelity design. Here a production sample of such solid-state devices is checked through a magnifier at Hughes Electronics Division.

and voices—a certain sonic sparkle and brilliance. It can make stereo so realistic that a blindfolded listener often can't tell the difference between reproduced music and the real thing.

With all these advantages, what has held transistors back for so long? You would think that both manufacturer and high-fidelity fan alike would have jumped on the bandwagon long ago.

Until very recently, transistors were an unfulfilled promise. The hi-fi industry wanted to exploit these new possibilities, but manufacturers were busy filling the needs of the space and computer industries. Transistors designed to meet computer requirements are not ideal for high-fidelity use, but recently, manufacturers began to develop transistor types suitable for audio applications. Next, they automated their production lines so that the price of these superior parts could compete with the price of tubes. With automation came a superior quality control of the transistors. This meant dependability of the product.

There was another result of this revolution. Transistors require altogether different circuitry than tube equipment does. "It's almost like having to learn a new language!" exclaimed one technician. Engineers had to do a lot of homework before they could translate the advantages of transistors into new and reliable equipment. This, too, took time and held back the hi-fi transistor market for awhile.

But lately there has been a veritable flood of transistor components. The new transistor amplifiers and tuners (Fig. 3-5) pack a lot of performance into smaller, cooler, and lighter designs. Transistors are very small items, but they have revolutionized the audio industry.

THE POWER PLAY

When you are shopping for an amplifier, one of the first things to decide is how much power you need. It is easy to say "the bigger the better" and avoid the question. Still, you can waste a lot of money on unnecessary power. You can save this cash for other components if you make up your power budget in advance.

The most widely advertised specification of an amplifier is its *power rating* or *output power*. The terms mean the same thing; they tell you how much power the amplifier can deliver to the speakers. This power is always expressed as a certain number of *watts*.

Fig. 3-5. Harman-Kardon joins the solid-state pioneers with the A-1000 stereo amplifier, a fully-transistorized job delivering 35 watts per channel with exceptional transient response. Beneath the amplifier is Harman-Kardon's matching stereo-FM tuner Model F-1000T, also fully transistorized.

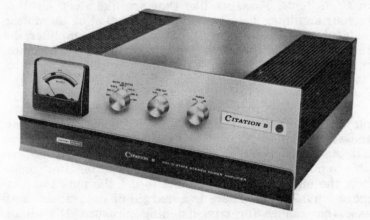

Fig. 3-6. A deluxe solid-state design employing separate power amplifier and preamplifier is Harman-Kardon's *Citation A* and *B*. Jointly, the two units provide about as good a performance as is attainable at the present state of technology. The units, also available factory-wired, offer unusually flexible control facilities.

What is the relationship between watts and loudness? Does a 60-watt amplifier play twice as loud as a 30-watt model? The answer is definitely no. If you had both of those amplifiers playing at full output, the 60-watt amplifier would sound only a little louder than the 30-watt.

Then why do we need all those extra watts? For an analogy, let's talk about cars. We all know that a 200-

horsepower car doesn't go twice as fast as a car with a 100-horsepower engine. What's more, you do not always run your car with the gas pedal pushed all the way down. You do not always demand every bit of available power from your engine. But you want a *power reserve* when you need it—and then you are very glad you have it. Because you have that reserve power, your car operates with less strain in ordinary situations.

The situation with amplifiers is very much like that. You may be listening to a soft passage played by strings. Suddenly the composer throws in trumpets and drums in *triple forte*. Passages like that are like steep hurdles to your amplifier, because the power content of the music suddenly surges upward. What does your amplifier do then? If your amplifier is too weak, the sound becomes rough, harsh, and noisy. But if your amplifier is equal to its task, the sudden climax won't faze it—the sound stays clear.

Suppose, now that we are comparing two amplifiers playing alternately through the same speaker. Even at the same volume, chances are that you will be able to pick out the more powerful one blindfolded. You may not be able to put your finger on *why* it sounds better. But somehow the bigger amplifier is able to get the music across more convincingly. There is a margin of naturalness and ease that makes for true listening pleasure. It's all in that power reserve.

It's true that the loudest passages in music often last only a moment or two. When they are over, the weak amplifier returns to its normal good behavior. But the effect of those momentary spells of harshness are stored up in the listener's subconscious memory. After a while he is left with an uncomfortable impression of the over-all sound texture. This is the main factor in listener fatigue—that odd feeling of discomfort and irritation that comes from overexposure to distorted sound. By contrast, an amplifier with sufficient power reserve glides easily and imperceptibly over any musical hurdles. Heavily scored passages remain transparent. The clarity of the sound is never compromised and no listener fatigue develops.

Another dividend from adequate power reserve is better bass. Higher-powered amplifiers are more likely to pump out a more realistic sound in the low range. You can get an idea of the amount of energy involved in really low notes if you think of the sheer physical force required to play the kettledrums, the tuba, or the bass fiddle. This energy finally reaches you in the form of extra watts. If your amplifier can handle this extra wallop, everything is fine. But many amplifiers tend to weaken in their low range. What happens in this case? The music is deprived of power in the very range where it is most needed. The amplifier is driven to distortion by the heavy bass. The sound loses its natural depth and solidity.

Since power reserve is so important, it pays to know just how much is enough. But before making specific recommendations, let us first see what the labels really mean when they tell us the power rating.

THE HOWS AND WHYS OF WATTS

The word *watts* is a measure of electric power (even if it was named for James Watt, the inventor of the steam engine). This measure can be used in different ways, so it is important to know what you are measuring. For instance, when you buy a 150-watt light bulb, the term watt tells you how much electrical power the bulb consumes. It does not tell you how much actual light the bulb will give you.

Audio amplifiers also have a given power consumption. This ranges from about 50 to 350 watts in, depending on which amplifier you have. But this figure only tells you how much electric power the amplifier needs to run. Do not confuse this with the number of watts of power that the amplifier will produce for your sound system. This is what really interests us: How many watts can the amplifier supply to the speakers?

There are a number of ways of rating this power output. It is important to know which one is being used when comparing the specifications of different amplifiers; otherwise, the figures will be downright misleading.

The best way of rating amplifiers is in the number of watts of *continuous power* that the amplifier can generate at its audio output (where it connects to the speakers). This is sometimes called *sine-wave power,* or *rms power.* As a measure of amplifier performance, this is perhaps the most critical one. It states the amount of power that can be delivered at all times without any ifs, ands, or buts.

Some manufacturers feel that this system does not give a fair picture of the way their amplifiers perform. Most amplifiers can exceed their rating for short bursts of power at musical peaks. Consequently, another method of measurement has been adopted, called the *music-power* rating. This takes into account the amplifier's ability to cover brief power bursts like cymbal crashes or drum beats. It follows that the music-power rating will be higher than the continuous-power rating of the same amplifier.

Occasionally you will find an amplifier rated as producing so many watts of *peak power.* This figure is noth-

Fig. 3-7. An inexpensive way to stereo is via Knight-Kit Model KG-320. This compact, solid-state amplifier delivers 16 watts per channel; it can be mail-ordered from Allied Radio, Chicago, Illinois.

ing but the continuous-power rating arbitrarily doubled. It conveys nothing but a misleading impression of the amplifier's abilities.

One practice that still prevails in the field of stereo amplifiers is the custom of adding together the power output of the two channels. For instance, an amplifier that delivers 50 watts per channel is called a 100-watt amplifier. In one sense this is a true statement. After

Fig. 3-8. Companion piece to the Knight-Kit KG-320 is the KG-70 all-transistor stereo fm-am tuner kit.

all, the amplifier does deliver a total of 100 watts, but this is misleading when you are trying to calculate your power needs. With such an amplifier, you will have only 50 watts (not 100) available for driving each speaker. Be sure you use the power rating *per channel* when you calculate your power needs.

Incidentally, the power ratings applied to amplifiers in ready-made consoles differs from those used by manufacturers of high-fidelity components. There is no need to take up the details of how these methods differ. It is enough to say that the amplifiers in consoles are vastly overrated when compared to individual components. You simply have to demand full specifications and read the fine print. There is no other way to buy ready-made phonographs and be sure you are getting your money's worth.

PICKING YOUR POWER

Two factors determine the power that your amplifier needs: (1) the size and character of your room, and (2) the type of speakers your amplifier must drive.

It is apparent that the bigger the room is, the more power you will need to fill it with music. This is not merely a matter of turning up the volume. Rather, it depends on that power reserve mentioned earlier. With sufficient power, the loud passages will fill the room without seeming to shout and screech.

The decorating scheme of a room also affects the power requirement. Rugs, pillows, upholstered furniture, and heavy draperies swallow up a lot of sound. To make up for this absorption, you need to pump more sound into the room, and this takes more watts. If, on the other hand, you live in a contemporary style, uncluttered interior with plenty of blank wall space, the sound is reflected from the plane surfaces. This saves power. The difference between the two styles of decor may add up to 50 percent of your power requirement.

The second factor (speaker type) is a bit more complex. When the amplifier feeds power to the speaker, the speaker turns only a part of this power into sound. Speakers that turn a large percentage of amplifier power into sound are called *high-efficiency speakers*. Those that turn only a small fraction of that power into sound are called *low-efficiency speakers*.

A speaker's efficiency is *not* a measure of its quality. Indeed, inefficient speakers usually sound better than high-efficiency designs. The term merely tells us something about the power consumption of the speaker. In general, speakers in horn enclosures are highly efficient. Speakers in bass-reflex baffles usually operate at medium efficiency. Speakers in sealed enclosures, such as most bookshelf type speakers, usually have low efficiency. Here are some typical power requirements for *an average size room with average acoustics:* high-efficiency speakers need 10 watts per channel, medium-efficiency speakers need 16 watts per channel, and low-efficiency speakers need 20 watts per channel.

The wattage should be doubled for rooms with dead acoustics (rooms with lots of upholstery, rugs, pillows, etc.). But these power recommendations can be cut by 25 percent for rooms with very live acoustics (rooms with lots of bare wall and a minimum of clutter). A couple of watts more or less will probably do just as well. **REMEMBER:** these recommendations are for the power of *each* stereo channel.

FREQUENCY RESPONSE

Wide range of frequency response is an important requirement in all the components of your system (except for your turntable and tone arm), yet it is often misunderstood. Simply to say an amplifier has a frequency range from 20 to 20,000 cycles does not mean very much. All that those figures tell you are the lowest and highest notes that the amplifier can reproduce. What interests us is *how well* does the component reproduce them *and all the other notes in between.* Does it reproduce all the notes (high, low, and in between) in the same proportion that they are heard in the studio? Does it stress some notes or swallow others? In other words, is its frequency response as *flat* as possible?

The term *flat frequency response* originates from the practice of showing this quality on a graph (Fig. 3-9). If all notes are reproduced evenly and proportionately, the graph comes out as a flat straight line. If the component favors certain frequencies disproportionately, this shows up as hump, or peak, on the graph. Such *response peaks* are a sign of poor equipment.

Actually we never get a straight-line graph. Perfectly flat response is only an ideal. All components deviate from truly flat response, but, in top-rank equipment, engineers have been able to keep this deviation so small that the human ear can hardly tell the difference. Devi-

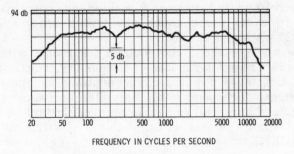

FREQUENCY IN CYCLES PER SECOND

Fig. 3-9. Typical response curve.

ation from flat response may be expressed in terms like this:

Response equals 30 to 20,000 cps ± 2 db

This means that for no frequency between 30 and 20,000 cps does the response go astray by more than two decibels (db). A decibel is a very small unit of loudness. It takes a loudness difference of about three *db* to be noticeable. Any deviation up to ± 1.5 db still comes within strict high-fidelity standards. But if that plus-or-minus figure

Fig. 3-10. A good bargain in terms of cost versus performance is the Knight KN-870 all-transistor amplifier. It can be mail-ordered in kit form from Allied Radio in Chicago. Its power output of 35 watts per channel is ample for most situations.

Fig. 3-11. A high-power solid-state kit is Lafayette's KT-950, which delivers 60 watts per channel with a frequency response from 10 to 25,000 cps at less than 1% distortion.

is greater than ± 3, or entirely lacking in the specifications of a component, be very suspicious.

TRANSIENT RESPONSE

A transient is a sound that appears with a sudden impact. Drum beats, cymbal crashes, piano chords, and plucked strings are examples of sounds that arrive with a bang. However, all transients are not so obvious; in fact, most of them are much more subtle. They represent the little differences in the way a guitarist plucks the strings, a fiddler uses his bow, or a flutist his tongue.

These swift delicate sounds present a challenge to an amplifier. It must react to them as fast as they appear, and drop them the instant they vanish. The ability to handle such sounds without blurring them we call *good transient response*. With sloppy transient response, an orchestra sounds soggy and dull instead of alive and exciting.

There is no easy way to measure transient response. As a rough rule, the wider and flatter the frequency response is, and the higher the power reserve, the sharper the transient response will be. For this reason, some amplifier designers have extended frequency response well beyond the limits of human hearing. Certain top-flight amplifiers boast a virtually flat frequency response from 5 to 100,000 cps, in order to ensure the best possible transient response. Still, flat response within ±2.5 db from 30 to 20,000 cps may be taken as an acceptable standard for a high-fidelity amplifier.

DISTORTION

If you have ever looked at yourself in a funny-house mirror, you saw a perfect illustration of what is meant by the term *distortion*. You saw in the mirror a complete

Fig. 3-12. Scott's Model 233 stereo amplifier offers 30 watts per channel with distortion of less than 1% and frequency response from 27 to 20,000 cps.

image of yourself. All the details were there. Still, the image was not true to the original. The same thing happens to the music signal when it is distorted in poor reproduction. The sound waves become twisted and cockeyed.

At its worst, distortion can make a violin screech like a set of bad brakes. But often it is more subtle than that. It is just barely noticeable, but the effect is like the Chinese water torture. After listening for a while, you feel the uneasy symptoms of listener fatigue. You feel a deep urge to "turn that darn thing off!"

Distortion is readily measured, and reputable manufacturers always state the amount of distortion in their amplifiers. Modern engineering has succeeded in keeping distortion so low that it is practically inaudible and doesn't bother the listener. For high-fidelity equipment, two types of distortion are usually stated in the specs. One is harmonic distortion; the other is intermodulation distortion, usually abbreviated IM. If neither type of distortion gets above two percent at full output, the amplifier is well within high-fidelity standards. But, in top-grade equipment, harmonic and IM distortion are one percent or less, which shows that the sound is not noticeably altered as it passes through the amplifier. Fidelity to the original music is maintained.

Fig. 3-13. Fisher's Model X-202-G is a tube model with 40 watts output per channel, delivered at less than 1% distortion, featuring many operating conveniences.

HUM

Back in our discussion of transistors we have already described the effects of hum. Hum results from several causes, but there is one easy way to spot it. Simply disconnect all input cables from the amplifier (tuner, record player, etc.). Keep the amplifier connected to its speakers. Turn the volume control about halfway up. Under these conditions your amplifier should remain almost silent.

You can't expect any amplifier to be perfectly hum free when the volume is turned all the way up, but even then the hum should not be obtrusive.

OPERATING FEATURES

When shopping for your amplifier, pick one that suits your particular needs. Make sure it has inputs for all the components you plan to use with it, such as tape recorder, record player, and tuner.

Individual models differ widely in the arrangement of their controls. A good amplifier should have separate treble and bass controls, an input selector, and a stereo-balance control. These are essential. Additional features, such as a stereo-blend control (to let you readjust the apparent stereo separation between the speakers), scratch and rumble filters, earphone connections, etc., are often convenient. A demonstration of all these controls at your audio dealer will help you decide which operating features you really want.

CHAPTER 4

THE SPEAKERS

A loudspeaker is a musical instrument. Its purpose, after all, is to make musical sounds. Speakers come in many shapes and sizes, and differ widely in price and performance. The finest amplifier sounds tinny if you play it through a poor speaker. If the speaker can't reproduce the full range of sound furnished by your amplifier, your investment in the amplifier is wasted.

A good speaker must meet three basic requirements: (1) It must cover the range of musical sound from at least 50 to 15,000 cps; as in the case of amplifiers, the response within this range should be uniform. (2) It must leave the original sound unchanged; poor speakers impose their own tone "coloration" on the music, altering the character of the various instruments. (3) The speaker must not blur the music or make it sound harsh; the sound must remain clear at all times.

Elements of personal taste in sound often enter into both speaker design and speaker buying. No two makes of speakers sound exactly alike. But these differences do not necessarily mean that one speaker is better than the other. Their dissimilarity may stem from a difference of opinion between their designers. One designer may favor a warmer, more mellow sound; another may stress brilliance and brightness. What you prefer should decide your choice.

Most of us have definite tastes in listening. Some people like to sit in the front row when they attend a concert. They generally prefer bright-sounding speakers which make them feel close to the source of the music. Others favor balcony seats where they get a more remote sound, but a better overall blend of singers and instruments. These listeners will probably select speakers with a more distant, warmer sound quality.

Disregarding personal tastes, perhaps the most important single factor in a speaker is clarity. As you listen to a speaker, ask yourself: Is the sound really smooth? Can you pick out the individual instruments in the orchestra? Is the sound free from that edgy quality that often passes for hi-fi on cheap equipment? When a lot of instruments are playing at once, does the passage sound unmuddled and clearly transparent?

Spurn speakers with an unnaturally "hoked-up" sound—boomy bass and shrill treble. That bigger-than-life sound is often the mark of an inferior speaker. What seems impressive at first hearing soon becomes a tiresome exaggeration. A really superior speaker seems less dramatic at first hearing, but it grows on you. After a while you appreciate its smoothness and sweetness of sound and its natural, rather than dramatic, quality. It is a good idea to shop for a speaker soon after hearing a concert. Then, with the sounds of real music still fresh in your ears, you will be able to tell a really "natural" speaker when you hear one.

Speaker advertising often emphasizes extended frequency response in the upper range. This is actually less important than clarity, and absence of false tone coloration. A natural balance between the high and low frequencies is also more important than extended highs. Without balance, a speaker may sound thin and shrill.

TWEETERS AND WOOFERS

Because a single speaker unit cannot efficiently cover the whole musical range from top to bottom, modern speakers usually employ two separate units—a tweeter for high notes, and a woofer for the low notes.

A woofer is usually a fairly big speaker and heavily constructed, so that its own natural resonance lies in the low bass range which it must produce. A top quality woofer should be able to reach the lowest notes of the orchestra (around 35 cps) without faltering. This lends a special feeling of warmth and depth to the reproduced music.

Fig. 4-1. Configuration of a big speaker system with the grill cloth removed shows four woofers topped by two midrange speakers and an array of tweeters at the top. This is a Bozak Model P310-A-6.

Tweeters, by contrast, are small loudspeaker units suited to the physical requirements for producing high notes. Their natural resonance lies in the high frequency region. This is due to their smaller size. A good tweeter must be free of spurious resonances (response peaks) that emphasize certain frequencies more than others. Otherwise it would sound shrill.

Most of today's speaker systems come fully assembled, with matching woofers and tweeters built in (Fig. 4-1). These systems also contain a so-called *crossover network*. This is an electric circuit which channels the highs to the tweeter and the lows to the woofer.

DISPERSION

Proper *dispersion* of high frequencies over a wide angle is too often neglected in evaluating speakers. If the

Fig. 4-2. The elements of the Acoustic Research AR-3—a top-quality bookshelf speaker—are visible with the grill cloth removed. An acoustic-suspension woofer is located at the left. Midrange and tweeter units are dome-shaped for wide-angle treble dispersion.

highs are projected in a narrow beam (like the headlights of a car) the speaker sounds tight and hard. A good speaker, one with adequate dispersion (Fig. 4-2), spreads its highs evenly around a room, giving a smoother, fuller sound in all parts of the room, not just directly in front of the speaker.

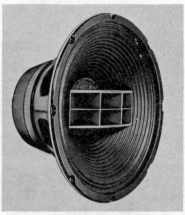

Fig. 4-3. This Jensen Model H-1380 speaker shows a typical coaxial design with the tweeter nestling inside the woofer. The large woofer cone projects the bass, the horn at the center handles the highs. The horn is divided into separate cells and shaped to achieve the widest possible dispersion of high frequencies.

A simple way to test for the dispersion of a speaker is to walk across the room. If the quality of the treble range changes drastically as you cross in front of the speaker, the chances are that it is too directional, that is, it has too little dispersion. A fair minimum angle of dispersion is about 120 degrees.

TRANSIENT RESPONSE

We have already described transient response in the chapter on amplifiers. If the speaker can't respond fast enough to the amplifier's quick transient signals, then your amplifier's quality will not come across in the sound you hear.

Here again, the test is to listen critically. Listen to sharp clicking sounds like those of percussion. The impact of the drumstick on the drumskin or on the wooden slats of the xylophone should sound hard and clear. A pianist's attack on a loud chord or a guitarist's plucking of the strings should sound sharply defined.

SPEAKER ENCLOSURES

A speaker enclosure, sometimes called a *baffle*, is just a box for your speaker. Without its enclosure, a speaker would sound thin; all the low notes would be missing.

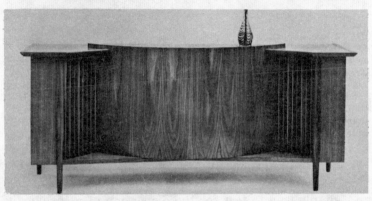

Fig. 4-4. James B. Lansing's luxurious *Metregon* is a complete stereo speaker system incorporating separate woofers, midrange, and tweeter units for each channel. The curved wooden surface at the center disperses the sound.

Nearly all speakers are sold nowadays as complete units (Fig. 4-4): woofers and tweeters in an acoustically matched enclosure. The size and shape of the enclosure may be important to you. For example, if you are cramped for space, you may want small compact speakers that fit into a bookshelf. If you have plenty of room you may want to try out some larger designs. Smaller speakers can put out just as much bass as big ones, however; thanks to modern baffle design, you can now get bass without bulk. Figs. 4-5 through 4-7 show various types of enclosures.

Fig. 4-5. Despite the fact that the best of today's bookshelf speakers give excellent bass, some people still prefer the full-sized floor models, such as this Wharfedale W90.

THE ACID TEST

One of the best ways to choose between two speakers is the so-called *A-B Test*. If your audio dealer doesn't know what this is, or is not equipped to perform it, find some other shop to run this test for you before you decide on any speaker.

The procedure is simple. First you listen to Speaker A, then to Speaker B with the same amplifier and the same music. Most of the larger high-fidelity shops have special switchboards to let you listen to almost any combination of components and switch instantly from one to the other for quick comparisons. If possible, you should listen to the speaker through the same type of amplifier that you intend to use it with. Pick an outstanding recording of orchestral music for your test, and make sure that the record is dust free. Try to compare the two speakers at the same or similar passages in the music.

As you listen, you might keep several questions in mind. Can you distinguish between the tuba and the double bass when they play together? Do the violins have a silken sheen? Is there solid weight in the sound of the cellos? Does the percussion sound crisp and sharp? Does the brass come through with a tingling edge but without harshness? Do the woodwinds have enough bite? Do all the notes in a piano chord sound clean and sharply focused? Questions of this type will help you spot the quality factors in speaker performance.

Fig. 4-6. Even speakers have been miniaturized recently, as demonstrated by this KLH Model 14-B, which handles nearly the full range of musical sound despite its bantam cabinet dimensions (14 × 8 × 8¼ inches).

Remember also that music doesn't always shout at you. A good speaker must be able to play soft passages just as convincingly as the loud ones. There must be no loss in clarity or change in coloration, whether the music is soft and calm, or whether it is grand and climactic.

Fig. 4-7. An unusual design is this Du-Kane corner speaker.

Price alone is not a satisfactory guide to merit. Nobody expects a $50 speaker to perform like a $200 one, but *some* $200 speakers sound no better than *some* $50 speakers.

Always demand clarity in the sound. If you buy a small inexpensive model, you may have to sacrifice some response in the extreme bass range, but you don't have to sacrifice clear, undistorted response within the frequency limits of a moderately priced speaker. Reject any speaker that has a fuzzy edge on the sound, but don't expect a small speaker to shake the walls with thunder.

One important rule in comparing loudspeakers: play them all at the same volume. If one speaker is louder than another adjust the volume or balance controls until the speakers match. If one speaker is played louder than the other, the ear will fool you and make you think that the louder one is preferable. Sometimes a salesman will play one speaker louder in order to persuade you to buy it. Whatever his reason, don't fall for this old trick of the trade. Make him match the speaker volumes and then compare.

Take your time. Hurrying through a test is no way to ensure your satisfaction. Relax, sit down, make yourself comfortable. Try to imagine that you are in your own home. If you are tired or irritable, postpone the test. Judging speakers takes concentration. Be sure you are in the proper frame of mind.

Remember, a flashy speaker will dazzle you at first, but you will soon tire of living with it day in and day out. Simple naturalness is the ideal.

Make certain that your amplifier has enough power to drive the speakers you choose. Conversely, make sure the speakers you choose can handle all the power put out by your amplifier.

Above all, keep in mind that your speakers are the final link in your sound system. More than any other component, they determine what you hear. They have the last word.

CHAPTER 5

THE TUNER

Everybody has a radio; as a matter of fact, there are more radios than people in this country! Still, if you haven't heard broadcasts reproduced in stereo high fidelity, you have a real surprise coming.

As you may know there are two general types of commercial broadcasting. The first is the standard a-m type of broadcasting. The other is fm, a growth of the postwar years, and a boon to the music-minded listener. F-m radio provides a wider frequency range than does am: it covers the whole musical frequency range; it has low distortion and virtually no static; it transmits music with a full dynamic range against a silent background. The same high quality of reception prevails, day and night, regardless of the weather.

A latest wrinkle in radio is stereo fm (also called f-m multiplex); this type of broadcasting is now spreading to all parts of the country. F-m stereo permits you to enjoy an extremely high quality of stereo realism through your own sound system. However, if you do not have a stereo system, these broadcasts can be heard as ordinary mono fm with no loss in quality.

To play broadcasts through your sound system, you need a tuner. A tuner is essentially a radio without its amplifier or speaker. Unlike ordinary radios, tuners are built to high-fidelity standards.

TUNER TYPES

There are several types of tuners which you may consider. There are receivers (that is, tuner-amplifier combinations) built into one unit (Fig. 5-1). If you do not yet own an amplifier, there may be an advantage for you in such a package. The new transistor designs are compact, cool-running, and stylish. These combinations connect with your record player, tape recorder, and speakers. If you already have a satisfactory amplifier, there is no point in duplicating its function.

Fig. 5-1. An increasingly popular type of component is the so-called stereo receiver, which combines on a single chassis a stereo tuner and amplifier. All you need to do is to hook up a record player and a pair of speakers to complete a stereo sound system. A recent model of this kind is the Scott 380-B.

There are tuners for fm only (Fig. 5-2) ; others provide for both a-m and f-m reception (Fig. 5-3). Most current tuners are equipped for stereo. The decision between types will depend on what kind of broadcasting is available in your locality.

If you live in a metropolitan area, you should have little use for an a-m tuner. Almost all of the a-m programs are also available on fm; there are very few exceptions to this. Unless these exceptions are programs

Fig. 5-2. One of today's best stereo f-m tuners is Scott's partly transistorized Model 312 with 2.2 microvolts usable sensitivity, which automatically switches between stereo and mono, depending on which station is tuned in.

you are particularly interested in, there is not much point in spending the extra money for am.

Over 1200 f-m stations are now in operation. More than a third of them broadcast at least a part of their programs in stereo, and the number of stereo stations is growing fast.

Fig. 5-3. The Heath AJ-32 kit offers both fm-stereo and a-m reception with an f-m sensitivity of 3.5 microvolts.

The extraordinary program quality of fm has great appeal for the fidelity-conscious listener. It is truly "hi-fi from the sky"—what's more it is free. F-m broadcasts supplement your record collection with an almost unlimited variety of high-fidelity programs. There are stations that play nothing but concert music. Others specialize in jazz or pops; still others offer bits of everything. Your audio dealer can probably tell you what f-m stations serve your area, and what kind of programing you can find on your dial.

Fig. 5-4. A partly transistorized tuner design is Fisher's TFM-300 with 1.8 microvolts sensitivity and a variety of operating features, including a squelch circuit.

ANTENNAS

Conditions for receiving fm are similar to those for TV. Reception depends on two factors: (1) the strength of the station, and (2) your own location. For instance, if your home is on high ground you will have better reception than if you live down in a valley. Depending on terrain, you can pull in a station over distances up to about 130 miles.

No tuner is better than its antenna. A good antenna pulls in distant stations more clearly. If you live in a city close to most f-m stations, an indoor antenna is probably all you will need. In the suburbs, a roof antenna is especially helpful for optimum sound quality in stereo. In fringe areas (near the limit of a station's strength), you may need a multielement antenna similar to the TV antennas used in such areas. Rotators and antenna boosters (like those used for TV) also improve f-m reception in different locations.

SENSITIVITY

Sensitivity is the ability of a tuner to pick up weak or distant stations. Sensitivity is not of primary importance if you live near the stations you want to receive. It makes a difference only if you are located in a fringe area. This is particularly true for stereo fm, which requires a stronger signal.

Audio manufacturers are competing with each other in a kind of "sensitivity race" very much like the "horsepower race" in the automobile industry. The result is that today's best tuners are very sensitive indeed. But remember, you may not really need that much sensitivity in your particular location. Sensitivity is usually reported as a number of microvolts (abbreviated μV). The smaller this number, the greater the sensitivity. For instance, a tuner with a sensitivity of 2 μV has more pull than a tuner with a rating of 4 μV. In urban areas, a sensitivity of about 4 μV should be satisfactory. At a distance of 25 miles, a rating of 3 will suffice. But for the fringe areas, ratings of 1.8 μV or less may be necessary.

QUIETING

Quieting is usually stated in db, the basic unit of loudness. You may, for instance, read a specification like this: sensitivity = 3 μV for 30-db quieting.

This means that the incoming signal must be 3 μV strong if your tuner is to reproduce it 30 db louder than the remaining level of noise or interference. Some sensitivity ratings are stated for 20-db quieting, which is not nearly as good.

USABLE SENSITIVITY

Since sensitivity in tuners must always be related to quieting, the *Institute of High Fidelity* has recently introduced a single measure to express both concepts. This is called *usable sensitivity*. It rates the sensitivity of a tuner for high-quality reception that contains no more than 3 percent noise and distortion. This measurement makes it possible for you to compare sensitivity ratings of different tuners because they are all referred to the same performance standard.

DISTORTION AND FREQUENCY RESPONSE

The total distortion in a good tuner should not exceed 1 percent at full tuner output. The distortion in a top quality tuner may measure less than half that figure.

The audio-frequency response of an f-m tuner need not extend beyond 15,000 cps, since this is the upper limit of f-m broadcasting. However, within that range, it should be *flat* to within ±1 db.

OTHER SPECIFICATIONS

You may find among f-m tuner specifications such entries as *discriminator bandwidth, i-f bandwidth, number of i-f stages, circuit configuration,* and other impressive bits of information. These details may interest an engineer, but it is difficult to understand their significance without a detailed knowledge of radio theory. Fortunately, none of these factors is of direct importance to the hi-fi listener. Their collective effect on performance is told by the performance factors we have already discussed: sensitivity and distortion.

However, there is one other characteristic that may be important if you live in a location where two fm stations happen to come in at the same spot on your dial. The ability of your set to separate these stations—bringing in the stronger signal without the interference of the weaker—is called *capture ratio*. This situation rarely arises unless you happen to live midway between two cities which happen to have fm stations transmitting on the same frequency. A tuner's capture ratio is expressed as the number of db (loudness units) by which two conflicting stations must differ if the tuner is to keep them apart. Thus the *smaller* the number, the *better* the capture ratio.

Do not confuse *capture ratio* with *selectivity*. Selectivity refers to your tuner's ability to keep apart stations *next to each other* on your dial. Capture ratio applies to situations in which two stations arrive at the *same point* on your dial.

AFC

The letters AFC stand for *automatic frequency control* which locks in the station to which you have tuned so that it can't "drift." This was extremely important on some of the older tuners which often wouldn't hold a station steady without AFC. Newer designs often do without AFC. They employ circuits known as *wideband detectors* that make the signal stay put.

It takes no special skill to tune in an f-m station. But you have to be careful to tune the station accurately. Sloppy tuning results in fuzzy sound. That's why most quality tuners have visual tuning indicators to tell you when you've got the station "right on the nose." Some of these indicators are of the "magic eye" type, others are in the form of a dial with a pointer that tells you when the station is accurately in tune. With the help of one of these indicators you can tune in your station even in complete silence. With your volume set at zero, you can turn the knob until the needle of your meter tells you when your station is in perfect focus. This saves you the trouble of listening to a lot of noise between stations. When you turn up the volume, your station comes in clearly right from the start.

Another interesting feature on some tuners is the *squelch*. A lot of noise is usually heard when tuning from one station to another. For this reason, designers have come up with a circuit that *squelches* this noise. But the squelch may also muffle weak stations. That's why such tuners come with a *Squelch Defeat* switch. This allows you to hunt for those weaker signals.

Stereo FM tuners have a special signal that tells you when a stereo broadcast is coming in. Usually it is a light that automatically flashes on when you hit a stereo station. Sometimes it is an audible "beep" which you can monitor by flipping a switch. Some tuners will automatically switch stereo to mono, and back again, depending on whether the station you are tuning in is broadcasting in stereo or mono.

Any good tuner, regardless of its particular operating features, makes a fine "skyhook" for your sound system. It pulls out of the air an endless supply of music and entertainment that is yours for free—and you hear it reproduced with all the sonic splendor that your amplifiers and speakers can provide.

CHAPTER 6

THE MOST FOR YOUR MONEY

It is easy to spend your money—the trick is to get the most for it. That takes intelligent shopping.

Buying sound equipment is like buying a car. If your budget is tight, you may think in Volkswagen terms—and still get excellent value for your money. A few extra bucks will buy you a Buick, and you get a smoother ride. If money is no object, get a Rolls-Royce.

Think of sound systems the same way: "VW" class, "Buick" class, and the "Rolls" class. Smart shoppers know what each class offers and what it costs.

The price range of high-fidelity components varies widely. A single component in the Rolls class, for example, may cost more than a whole sound system in the VW class. You have to decide at which point in the price scale you can satisfy both your ears and your bankbook.

To begin with, let's spell out two guiding principles: (1) All modern components are stereo. If you buy mono equipment, you are tying up your money in obsolete gear. (2) One advantage of buying component systems is that you can start out with inexpensive units and later upgrade your system, one component at a time. This spreads your investment.

With this in mind, examine what each of the price classes offer you. Then decide which best suits your requirements and your budget.

THE "VW" CLASS

The lowest price of admission to component stereo hi-fi is around $250. This figure will provide for a pair of speakers, a stereo amplifier, and a *program source*. By program source we mean either a record player or a tuner. High-fidelity tape machines are too expensive to consider in this class. It may be possible to get components at a good discount, winding up with both tuner *and* record player within this budget. It depends on your dealer and your haggling talent.

A few excellent speakers are now available in the $50 to $70 price range. They may not reach bottom bass, but their overall clarity is fine. Such speakers are usually of the low-efficiency type. Be absolutely sure that your amplifier delivers enough power to drive them.

A low-cost amplifier in the $50 to $80 price range usually supplies about 15 to 18 watts per channel. This is the least you can consider for use with the speakers suggested above.

Excellent turntable–tone–arm combinations are available for from about $60 to $70. Some fairly good automatic turntables can be had for about the same price. You can get a high-compliance cartridge for less than $20 that will match the overall quality of such a low-budget sound system.

Stereo tuners are priced from $80 up. You can find attractive bargains of all kinds of low-cost equipment advertised in electronic mail-order catalogs. You might do well to study these catalogs before making up your mind.

What kind of performance does such a system offer? in normal-size rooms, at normal listening volumes, it should provide a great deal of pleasure. The bass may lack a degree of conviction. The limited power reserve will not let you shake the walls, but the musical quality will be pleasing and natural—far better than that of ordinary radios and phonographs costing much more.

Fig. 6-1. This entire Heathkit rig including the cabinet was built from kit parts.

"BUICK" CLASS

There is no compromise in this group. At a cost ranging from about $450 to $600, it offers solid respectability in sound. Equipment in this class meets all but the most sophisticated tastes. A typical price breakdown for the individual components in such a system might run as follows:

Tone arm + turntable	$ 60—$100
Cartridge	$ 25—$ 50
Amplifier (25 to 35 watts per channel)	$120—$160
Speakers (each)	$100—$150
Tuner	$130—$150
Total	$435—$610

With this class of equipment you should be able to listen without even being aware of the equipment. All you think about is the music itself. That is the ultimate test of a good sound system.

The equipment in this class should offer extra conveniences normally not found on less expensive models—outputs for extension speakers in other rooms, blend controls to adjust the stereo spread, earphone terminals, etc. You may want to add a tape recorder, but that will raise the ante by at least another $100 to $200.

Most listeners are fully satisfied by equipment in this class. Beyond this level of performance, further improvement is only slight and costly. Up to the "Buick" class,

Courtesy Harman-Kardon, Inc.

Fig. 6-2. Simple step-by-step instructions make kit-building almost foolproof, providing you follow the instructions carefully.

performance improves noticeably with increased price. Beyond this point you run into diminishing returns on your investment: cost increases faster than performance. But if you must have a "Rolls" and nothing else will do, break the bank (or at least your bank account) and step right up to the elite.

"ROLLS" CLASS

Here you get superb sound with an extra bonus—the sheer pride and joy of knowing you have the best. To some people that's all that counts. But if you are counting dollars, too, here's the bill:

Turntable + tone arm	$ 150—$300
Cartridge	$ 50—$ 70
Amplifier (50 watts per channel)	$ 500—$700
Tuner	$ 300—$500
Speakers (each)	$ 225—and up
Total	$1275—and up

Don't think you can't top these prices; you can pay more than $1000 for a pair of speakers alone. But if music is your passion and you own some oil wells, it's worth it. Wouldn't you really rather have a Rolls?

SMART MONEY

If you have to juggle your hi-fi budget, it's handy to know where a few dollars will do the most good.

One guidepost: Buy the best speakers you can afford—even if you have to skimp on other components. A modest amplifier, for example, still sounds respectable within its power limits. But the quality of this signal can be ruined before it reaches your ears through a hoarse-voiced speaker.

This doesn't mean that you have to plunk down $300 per speaker; you can get fine musical quality for less than half that amount. Critical listening is the only way to find out which speaker most pleases your ears.

Usually you can upgrade the sound of your system with a better cartridge. If your speakers are good, a few dollars on the cartridge may bring improvement.

As for amplifiers, remember, power reserve helps. Still you don't want to spend money on more power than you really need. Here are a few pointers to help you gauge your power requirements:

Live Acoustics

Live acoustics is due to large areas that reflect sound instead of absorbing it: floors of tile or linoleum; uncovered wooden floors; smooth walls; no heavy curtains, or clutter. Such an acoustic environment makes sound louder. In rooms like this, 15 watts per channel should suffice for low-efficiency speakers; 8 watts per channel will be adequate for high-efficiency speakers.

Average Acoustics

Average acoustics occurs, where there is an average floor area only partly covered by rugs and curtains, but no heavy drapes; little heavy upholstery; uncluttered furniture arrangement; or typical rooms with ceilings of average height. Under these average conditions, low-efficiency speakers will require perhaps 20 watts per channel; high-efficiency speakers will require perhaps 10 watts per channel.

Dead Acoustics

Dead acoustics is found in areas where there is wall-to-wall carpeting; heavy drapes; heavy upholstery; or pillows and wall hangings. Such furnishings in a room soak up lots of amplifier wattage. You may need 40 watts per channel or more to drive low-efficiency speakers. Even with high-efficiency speakers, you will need about 20 watts per channel. These figures apply to a listening room of not more than 30 feet in length or width (ceilings are assumed to be of normal height). For larger rooms, these ratings will have to be increased.

The suggested power ratings allow you to play symphonic orchestrations at full concert volume. However, intimate chamber music or jazz combos make considerably lighter demands on your equipment. If your taste runs in those directions you can cut somewhat on the power rating by about one fourth in each case.

CONSOLE CONSOLATIONS

If you prefer to buy a prepackaged console phonograph, designs are available to match different home decoration styles. But bear in mind the deficiencies of ready-made consoles. As a rule, their speaker baffling is inadequate. You can't move the speakers far enough apart for optimum stereo separation. Many consoles tend to skimp in the quality of the tone arm and turntable.

Courtesy Harman-Kardon, Inc.

Fig. 6-3. Kits are "housewife-tested." Before being sold to customers, audio kits are given to women who have never built hi-fi kits before. If they can complete the project, chances are that anyone can.

Console phonographs rarely live up to the specifications outlined in this book. Unless specified in technical detail, the merits of ready-made phonographs may not be what you are expecting.

Component systems allow you a greater range of choice, and the possibility of tailoring your choice of each component to your preference.

If choosing your own components is too much trouble, consoles offer the advantage of being easier to find and easier to buy. Most important for some people, you simply plug them in and they play. But you can't always count on getting *real* high-fidelity stereo.

KITS CUT COSTS

Maybe you don't mind a little manual labor in putting your system together. You don't have to be an electronics

Courtesy Harman-Kardon, Inc.

Fig. 6-4. Seeing the circuit take shape under your own hands greatly adds to the enjoyment of your components—providing you have the patience necessary for assembly work.

expert. Anybody can learn to solder a clean joint. And that's all it takes to build your equipment from kits. Step-by-step instructions that completely eliminate guesswork come with each kit. They are easy to read, easy to understand, and require no previous experience in electronics. All you need is a little patience and a love for building things. If you lack either of these qualities, chances are you won't finish the job.

If you are a do-it-yourselfer, you can save about one-third of the cost of your system. A soldering iron, a roll of solder, a screwdriver, and a pair of pliers are all the tools you need. This often makes it possible for you to own equipment that you couldn't otherwise afford.

Kits, nowadays, are practically foolproof, but some projects are more difficult than others. Complicated wiring often takes a good deal of patience. Tuners used to be the most difficult, but they have been greatly simplified recently. All the critical parts are now preassembled at the factory. Your dealer usually knows whether the kits he sells are hard to build. He can usually advise you about what it takes to tackle a project.

CHAPTER 7

THE HOOK-UP

Once you've got your components, you'll have to decide where to place them. One of the great advantages of having separate components is that you can put them where they look and sound best. Unlike bulky consoles, they usually fit on shelves and take up no floor space.

In setting up a stereo system, a few basic rules should be observed. Rule One: Keep your components cool. Don't, for instance, put your tuner on top of your amplifier. The heat from the amplifier will bake it just enough to throw its adjustments out of kilter. If your components are housed, or stashed away, in a tight space, they might easily overheat. Make sure they get enough ventilation. Allow at least an inch of space between the open back of any cabinet and the wall. If the back of the cabinet is enclosed, cut vents in it.

Next decide on your speaker placement, taking into account the position of your favorite chair. In general, stereo speakers are placed from 8 to 12 feet apart in average-size rooms. The optimum listening position is across the room from the speakers, close to the midpoint between the speakers. However, this pattern need not be observed strictly. Contrary to popular belief, you need not sit exactly in the middle of the speakers. Stereo allows the listener much more freedom in choosing a convenient listening spot than is generally assumed. Don't feel hemmed in by the geometry of stereo.

Fig. 7-1. Keeping components cool greatly prolongs their life. This is not usually a problem with transistor equipment, which does not develop much heat. Tube components, however, must be well ventilated. If they are housed in cramped quarters, a small fan might be used to disperse the heat. The unit shown here is a quiet-running model obtainable at most high-fidelity dealers.

Hooking up a high-fidelity system is almost as simple as plugging in a lamp. The trick is to know just which connection goes where. This is not difficult if you keep your mind on the basic logic of the system. Visualize the path of the audio signal as it travels from one component to another and finally emerges from the speaker.

This logic is best understood by classifying the components according to their function. First there are "program sources." These are the components that originate the signal you hear. This group includes record player, tuner, and tape recorder (if you have one).

The signals coming from these program sources must be connected to the *inputs* of the amplifier. The amplifier is the center of your whole system. (If you use a separate preamplifier and power amplifier, it is the preamplifier that acts as the clearing house for all the audio input signals).

CONNECTING THE PROGRAM SOURCES

Each stereo signal arrives at the amplifier input by a pair of cables—one cable for the left channel, and the other for the right channel. Often the left channel is marked Channel A, and the right one is marked Channel B. Sometimes the cables or plugs for each channel are color coded. A common, (but not always used) code is to color the plugs for the right channel red. (It is easy to remember: *red = right*.)

Record Player

Install the cartridge first. To do this connect the leads of the tone arm's cartridge shell to the appropriate pins on the rear of the cartridge (the manufacturer's instructions for both of these elements will tell you which leads go where). Next fasten the cartridge into the tone arm shell according to the instructions. Then level your turntable, using a spirit level.

Next, balance the tone arm at the proper tracking force for your cartridge. To do this you will require a *stylus gauge* obtainable at your dealer's for a nominal price. Some arms have a built-in gauge. Other arms often come with a separate gauge supplied as standard equipment.

Now turn to the cables coming out the tone arm. The signal cables will usually have small pointed pin plugs at the ends.

The two pin plugs (described above) should be connected to the proper input of the amplifier. If you have a magnetic phonograph cartridge, this will have the input marked "magnetic" (or, "mag"). If you have a ceramic cartridge, look for the input marked "ceramic" (or "cer").

When connecting the leads from the tone arm, identify left and right channel plugs; insert them into their respective channels. Also be sure that they are seated firmly in their receptacles and make contact at the outer rim (as well as on the center pin). If the contact is loose, a loud hum will result.

Sometimes another cable *without* a pin plug at the end of it comes out of your tone arm. This is a ground wire; its purpose is to minimize hum in the hook-up. This ground wire may be attached to any convenient spot on the chassis (the metal base plate of the amplifier). Usually a chassis screw provides a convenient attachment point.

The remaining wires coming from your record player are the regular electrical power line with an ordinary house-type plug at the end. Most amplifiers have what are called "convenience outlets" which are like ordinary wall sockets. Plug the power cord of your turntable into one of these.

Tuner

As a rule, your tuner will not have a cable leading from it. Instead, it will have pair of small round sockets marked "output." To connect this to your amplifier you need what is called a *patch cord*, which is a cable with a pin plug at each end. You can buy patch cords in various lengths from your audio dealer at a nominal price. One end of these patch cords is inserted in the tuner and the other end goes to the integrated amplifier at the input terminals marked "tuner" or "radio." Stereo tuner cables should go to the inputs marked "FM-MPX" (FM-multiplex). The power cord of your tuner can go either to a wall socket or to another convenience outlet at the back of your amplifier.

CONNECTING THE AMPLIFIER
TO THE SPEAKERS

NEVER TURN ON THE AMPLIFIER until the speakers are hooked up. It may do serious damage to the amplifier to run it without the speakers connected to it.

To connect your speakers to the amplifier, use ordinary lamp cord. Attach a suitable length of lamp cord to the terminals at the rear of each speaker. The other end goes to the output connections of your amplifier.

Fig. 7-2. Typical output connection between amplifier and speakers. Ordinary lamp cord connects speakers to amplifier. Follow instructions given in manufacturer's operating manual to assure proper speaker phasing and impedance matching.

These are usually two strips of screw terminals at the back of the amplifier. One of these strips is the output for the right-channel speaker, and the other is for the left-channel speaker. Each screw terminal on these strips is identified by number. The usual markings follow this pattern. Sometimes the letter C (which stands for "Common") or a zero is used to show the ground connection. The appropriate terminals to use depend on the *impedance* of your speaker. This electrical measurement is usually marked on the back of your speaker. If not, it is usually given in the instructions packed with the speaker.

Fig. 7-3. Typical input connection to an amplifier. Cables from program sources terminating in pin plugs are inserted into ring-shaped receptacles. Upper connection is for left channel (Channel A), lower connection for right channel (Channel B).

We will assume that your speaker has an impedance of 8 *ohms* (ohms are the units in which impedance is measured). Take the wire from the speaker terminal marked (+). Connect this to the screw terminal marked 8 (or whatever the impedance of your speaker happens to be). The other lead from this speaker is marked (−). This should be connected to the 0 or C screw terminal of the *same channel*. This procedure is the same for both speakers.

Before you tighten the screw terminals, twist the wire ends neatly so that no loose strands stick out. If the strands from one terminal touch the strands from another, it would cause a short circuit and damage your amplifier.

Speaker Phasing

The two stereo speakers must work in tandem, or, as it is called, *in phase*. Their cones must move together, that is, pushing and pulling the air at the same time. If one speaker pushes while the other pulls, the bass will be weakened.

The only easy way to tell whether your speakers are properly in phase or not is to listen carefully. Then flip the phase reverse switch on your amplifier. Compare the sound at these two settings. The setting which has the fuller bass and the smoother overall sound is the right one. If your amplifier doesn't have a phase reverse switch, reverse the positions of the wires at the back of *one* of your speakers. (This accomplishes the same thing.) Compare the sound in these two positions. Turn off your amplifier while switching speaker connections.

One last point—don't put your turntable on the same shelf with your speakers. Otherwise, speaker vibrations will cause a considerable disruption of the sound. This disruption is called *acoustic feedback*. It occurs when the speakers' vibrations get back to the tone arm. The phono stylus then picks up these vibrations with the ones recorded in the record grooves and feeds them back into the amplifier and speaker (and the whole thing goes around again and again). This disruption can range from a mild tonal blurring to an ear-splitting howl.

If you are using a separate preamplifier and power amplifier, it is of course necessary to make the connection between these components. This is done with patch cords in the same manner as that described for the tuner.

Fig. 7-4. Adding a tape recorder to your sound system lets you tape mono or stereo off the air from your tuner, copy your friends' records, or record "live" in your living room. The tapes are then reproduced in full fidelity through your component-type amplifier and speakers. Shown here is an Ampex Model 865, a fully transistorized design.

Here again, be sure that your cables connect from the right-channel output of the preamp to the right-channel input of the power amplifier. The same applies, naturally, to the left channel.

SUMMARY

No single book can tell you everything about a subject. This one tries to tell you what you want to know, what you need to know, and how to plan your system intelligently.

When you go shopping, remember your objectives. Keep in mind what your needs are and measure them against your budget. A $100 cartridge in a kiddie phonograph, for example, does nothing that a kiddie cartridge can't do. It's a matter of balancing factors to fit your taste, your plans, and your purse.

Remember also that an *A-B Test* is the most important one you can make when comparing components. If you can't hear it (after listening attentively for a while) there is no point in paying for it. But even an A-B Test can be a pitfall. If you use only one kind of record (say, folk-singers) for your test, you can't make a valid decision. Your test should include full symphonic orchestral passages (loud and soft), piano music (with some slow chords), organ music (low and slow), percussion passages (alternating with silence). Do not try to choose components while your ears are still ringing from a ride on the subway. Before you listen, try to imagine what sounds alive and clear. Listen critically and objectively, and **DON'T** let yourself get carried away by the music; listen to the *sound* and decide.

If you don't understand the controls on a unit you are considering, ask to have them fully explained to you. Ask yourself whether you need all the refinements you find on a model. If not, perhaps you can get a superior component by sacrificing the gadgets. At the same time, consider how a piece of equipment will fit your future plans. Will it have all the controls you need for your future operations, or will it force you to change your plans?

Your sound system is really a *music system;* use it musically. If you play guitar solos louder than a real live brass band, you can expect distortion. And don't expect your system to sound well with badly recorded or poorly preserved records. By the way, keep your records clean! See that they are kept free of finger marks and dust. Your audio dealer can show you many easy methods for doing this. A good sound system will play everything on your records—that includes the dust and grime. There are times, in soft, soothing music, when a tiny speck of dust can sound like a four-inch firecracker!

Dust is to records as germs are to your health; dust will make your records sick beyond recovery. It will eat little bites out of the record grooves, leaving the record permanently scarred, and then it is too late for cleaning.

The audio industry has come a long way since the wind-up *Victrola*. The refinement of modern stereo seems almost supernatural by comparison. Indeed, hi-fi is like the genie in the bottle. If you use it sensibly, it remains music's most obedient servant.